Look and Find®

Disney · PIXAR
FINDING NEMO

Illustrated by Art Mawhinney

Cover illustration by
the Disney Storybook Artists

Published by
Louis Weber, C.E.O.
Publications International, Ltd.
7373 North Cicero Avenue
Lincolnwood, Illinois 60712
Ground Floor, 59 Gloucester Place, London W1U 8JJ

Customer Service: customer_service@pilbooks.com

www.pilbooks.com

p i kids is a trademark of Publications International, Ltd.,
and is registered in the United States.
Look and Find is a trademark of Publications International, Ltd.,
and is registered in the United States and Canada.

8 7 6 5 4 3 2 1

Manufactured in China.

ISBN: 978-1-4508-5633-1

pi kids®   publications international, ltd.

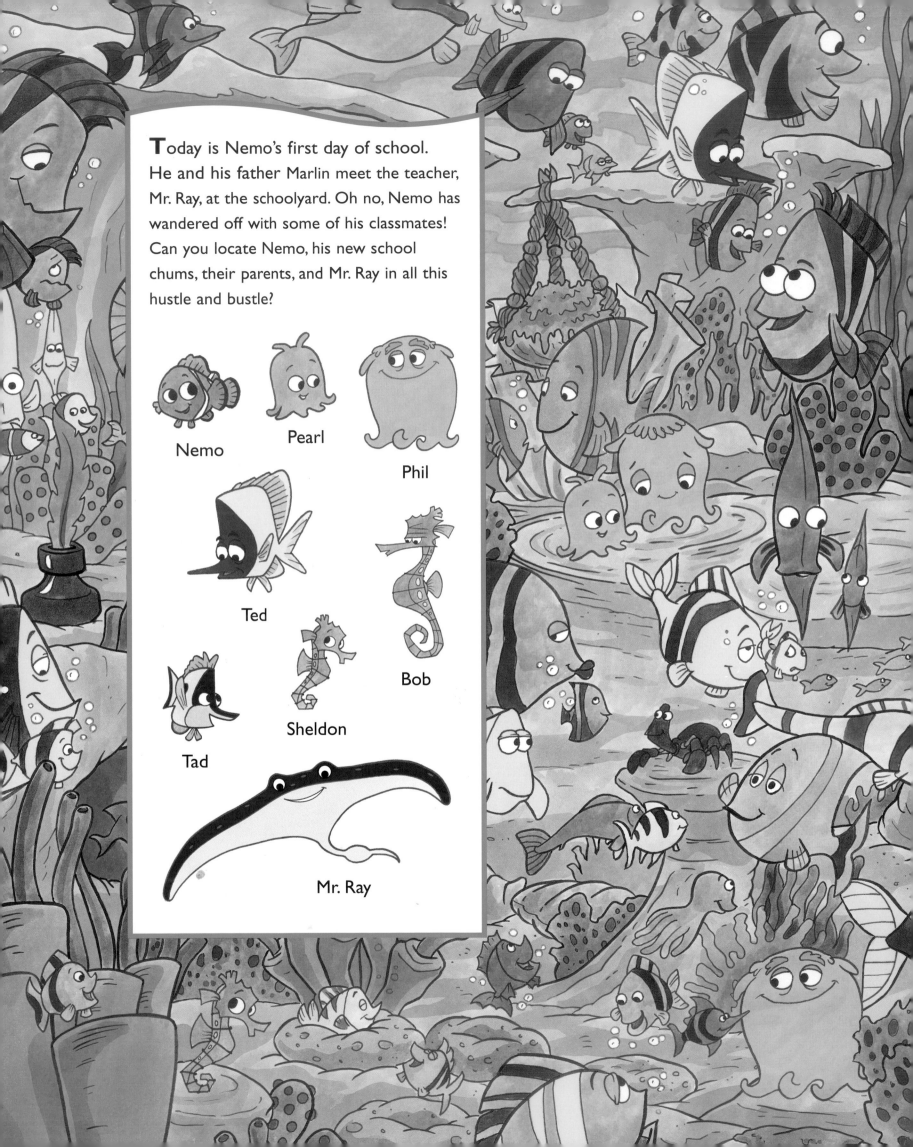

Today is Nemo's first day of school. He and his father Marlin meet the teacher, Mr. Ray, at the schoolyard. Oh no, Nemo has wandered off with some of his classmates! Can you locate Nemo, his new school chums, their parents, and Mr. Ray in all this hustle and bustle?

Nemo

Pearl

Phil

Ted

Bob

Tad

Sheldon

Mr. Ray

Nemo wandered too far away and is captured by a human diver! Marlin and his new friend, Dory, go into dangerous waters to look for clues that will help them find Nemo. Keep an eye out for these dangerous-looking sharks skulking about in the underwater minefield. Will Marlin and Dory make it through safely?

Bruce

Chum

Anchor

A basking shark

A sand shark

A whale shark

A tiger shark

Nemo is placed into a fish tank. As it turns out, the diver who caught him is actually a dentist who loves fish! But life in an aquarium is not much fun. Help Nemo and the other fish in the tank pass the time by finding all these things in the dentist's waiting room:

Dentists' Daily newspaper

A tooth mug

A fish painting

Swedish fish

Fish crackers

A fish lunchbox

A rainbow fish

There is an address on a diver's mask Marlin and Dory find near the sub: "P. Sherman, 42 Wallaby Way, Sydney." But how will they get there when they can barely read? Some helpful moonfish make quite an "impression" by pointing the pair in the right direction. Can you help Marlin and Dory spot these other impressive moonfish signs?

"Swordfish"

"Octopus"

"Shark"

"Sea turtle"

"Starfish"

"Lobster"

"Whale"

Marlin and Dory take a wrong turn, and now they're in the middle of a giant forest of jellyfish! Using your finger, trace the way out without touching any of their stinging tentacles. *Ouch!*

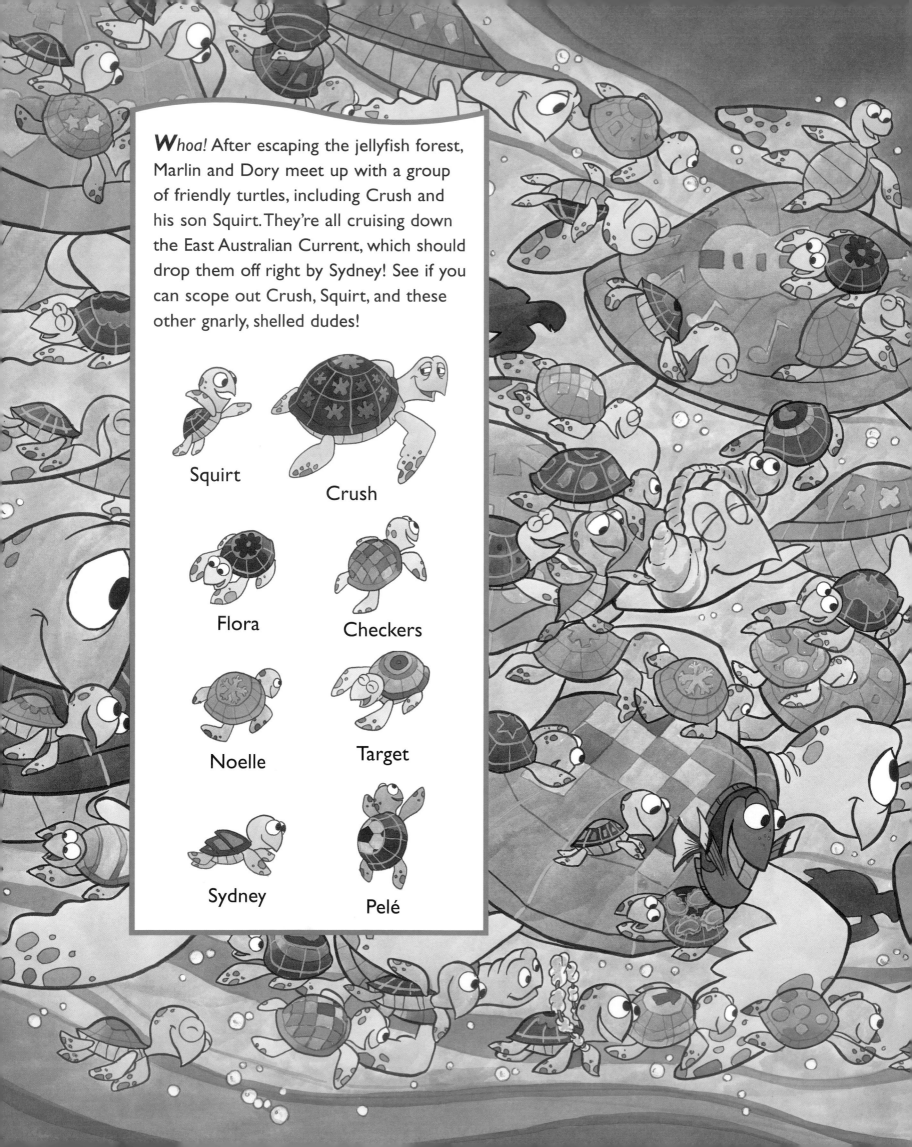

Whoa! After escaping the jellyfish forest, Marlin and Dory meet up with a group of friendly turtles, including Crush and his son Squirt. They're all cruising down the East Australian Current, which should drop them off right by Sydney! See if you can scope out Crush, Squirt, and these other gnarly, shelled dudes!

Squirt

Crush

Flora

Checkers

Noelle

Target

Sydney

Pelé

Once they get to Sydney, a nice pelican named Nigel takes Marlin and Dory to the dentist's office—just as Nemo and his new aquarium friends stage a daring escape! Gill, the leader of the Tank Gang, helps Nemo make his way to the spit sink, because "all drains lead to the ocean." As he flips and flops his way to safety, look around for all these other toothy things!

Exam gloves

A set of teeth

A set of X rays

Dental floss

Toothpaste

A toothbrush

Back in the ocean, Marlin and Nemo are reunited at last—but the excitement is not over, yet! The two clownfish help a netful of fish pull off an escape of their own from some local fishermen. Now the grateful groupers are showering the pair with thanks! Can you find Marlin, Nemo, and these other fish in this seaworthy celebration?

Marlin

Nemo

This grouper

Dory

This grouper

This grouper

Swim on back to the reef to find these school-related things:

❏ jar of squid ink
❏ stones in the shape of pluses and minuses
❏ seaweed macrame
❏ algae map of Australia

Peach, the starfish, gets really bored with her face up against the tank glass all day. Can you count how many of these things she can see in the dentist's waiting room?

___ flowers on the wallpaper
___ stuffed animals
___ seashells
___ toothbrushes
___ cans of fish food

Go back to the submarine with Bruce and his vegetarian friends. Over the years, many divers have tried to explore the sunken sub, but for some reason they can't get out of there fast enough! Can you spot the things the divers left behind?

❏ diver's fin
❏ diver's mask
❏ underwater flashlight
❏ weight belt
❏ scuba tank
❏ underwater camera

Those helpful moonfish have even more great impressions than the ones they showed Marlin and Dory. Can you find these, too?

❏ "anchor"
❏ "sailboat"
❏ "diver"
❏ "arrow"
❏ "pirate flag"
❏ "life preserver"

Go back to the jellyfish forest. If you look closely, some of the jellies look different from the rest. Can you spot these strangely familiar jellyfish?

❏ a moon jelly
❏ a jelly fish
❏ a jelly roll
❏ a peanut-butter-and-jellyfish
❏ a jelly mold
❏ a strawberry jelly

Go back and visit Crush, Squirt, and the rest of the sea turtles. Can you find these other distinctive shell patterns on some of the sea turtles riding the East Australian Current?

❏ a map of Australia
❏ a sand dollar
❏ a spider web
❏ a hopscotch board
❏ a palm tree

The dentist likes to spoil his bratty little niece, Darla. Go back to the dentist's office and try to find these presents he bought for her birthday:

❏ a doll
❏ a beach ball
❏ a baton
❏ a box of socks
❏ a pair of roller skates

Not long after Nemo escapes, it seems the rest of the Tank Gang make their way to freedom, as well! Turn back a page and try to find them as they swim back into the Big Blue.

Gill

Jacques

Peach

Bloat

Gurgle

Deb (and Flo)

Bubbles